MW00582387

Mothering
the
Crescent
Moons

Mothering the Crescent Moons

Our Journey with Sickle Cell Anemia

TYRENE GIBSON

with contributions by
AYA GIBSON TAYLOR

Books may be purchased in bulk quantity and/or special sales by contacting the publisher.

Published by Mynd Matters Publishing
715 Peachtree Street NE
Suites 100 & 200
Atlanta, GA 30308
www.myndmatterspublishing.com

978-1-957092-08-9 (pbk)
978-1-957092-09-6 (hdcv)
978-1-957092-10-2 (ebook)

FIRST EDITION

To my daughter Aya, I love you pumpkin!
May you always be blessed!

To Marc, thank you for giving Aya a new life. Be The
Match® totally changed my life, as well as my
daughter's life.

To my mom, Frankie Martin, thank you for your
time, love, and support.

To Dr. Krajewski, thank you for being an amazing
doctor.

To all the nurses & staff at Hackensack Meridian
Joseph M. Sanzari Children's Hospital, thank you!

Contents

I'm in pain.

Somebody help me!

My body can't take it.

I'm on fire!

I can't even get up or go to school.

It's hard to even feel the pain.

I hate having to live with the pain!

—Aya Gibson Taylor

CHAPTER 1

Sleepless Nights

"Breathe! Breathe, Aya! Breathe! You have to breathe, baby!" Imagine sitting in a recliner in a hospital room, thinking you are watching your child breathe their last breath. I, unfortunately, don't have to imagine. With tears rolling down my face, I could only watch as the monitor showed a decline in my daughter's heart rate, her oxygen levels went down, and pain medicine dripped intravenously into her arm. I screamed at the nurses and doctor, "She needs help! She can't breathe!"

Aya was sweating from a fever. Her lips were turning white, and her temperature was rising. I was panicking. Crazy thoughts ran through my mind. She was going into acute chest syndrome. Her hemoglobin had dropped, and they needed a chest X-ray. The doctor and nurses tried to prop her up in the wheelchair for the ride to get the X-ray, but she was so weak and in so much pain. She screamed, "I can't sit up! I can't sit up! It hurts! It hurts! Mommy, help! They're hurting me!"

From the time I had called for help to the time radiology came to take her for the X-ray, three or four hours had gone by, which was a long time to watch my child deteriorate. I was pissed and felt like a ticking time bomb. I also knew my baby had pneumonia. When they came to tell me she had to be taken to the ICU for twenty-four-hour care, I wasn't surprised. She had to have respiratory treatments and a blood transfusion. The first twenty-four hours were the most critical.

I barely recognized Aya because the drugs had taken over her body but it was the only way to alleviate the pain. I've often tried to imagine the worst pain I have ever experienced to comprehend the level of pain she must have felt, but I don't think I will ever know or fully understand.

The medicine caused her to become sleepy and

delirious. Sometimes, when she tried to talk, she slurred her words, making it difficult to decipher what she was trying to say. It was hard for her to function. Many times, I popped up out of the chair I was sitting in just to put my ear next to her mouth and listen to her breathe. I'd say to myself, *Another sleepless night!* I used to think that if I fell asleep, something might happen, and I wouldn't be awake to help my daughter. It was often in those moments of fear, doubt, and fatigue that Aya would cry out for me, "Mommy! Mommy!"

"When I see my mom sitting there crying, I feel sad for her. My mom has to see her daughter in so much pain."

—Aya Gibson Taylor

CHAPTER 2

An Unexpected Blessing

Hakim and I met through a mutual friend at Lightyear Entertainment in New York City. Hakim was running the radio promotions department and I was working as a Screen Actors Guild television agent running the television department for ID Model Management. Previously, I had worked for J. Michael Bloom at Ford Model for ten years.

The job was very demanding and challenging because I started and developed the entire television division. I had to devote a lot of time to entertaining clients and models after work. Hakim would also work late, so we would often meet up at his office. We hit it off right away and things quickly developed into a romantic relationship.

On our first trip together, we were supposed to

go skiing in Killington, Vermont, but we never made it to the slopes. Instead, we went into town visiting local restaurants and bars. Overall, it was a romantic and relaxing weekend and the trip brought us closer together.

We'd met in December 2000 and in February 2001, Hakim took me away for my birthday. We went to the Pink Sands Resort in Harbor Island, Bahamas. The resort had twenty-five pastel-colored cottages scattered on lush tropical grounds, along a three-mile stretch of a powder-pink sand beach. The island and beach were beautiful. We went swimming every day and enjoyed the food and nightlife.

While there, we noticed that I started to get sleepy by eight-thirty at night. Hakim and I were not quite sure what was going on, but this was not normal for me. Although I had a nice birthday, I didn't enjoy the trip as much as I thought I would because I really didn't feel like myself. When we got back to New Jersey, I had a beautiful glow so I decided to see my doctor. Dr. Mazlin, located on the Upper East Side of Manhattan, examined me and after taking a pregnancy test, I learned that I was pregnant.

I was shocked and initially, couldn't believe the news. I was excited and happy to become a mother, something I had always wanted, but I was still in denial. Could this really be happening now?

My breasts grew and I felt tired and nauseous every day. It was awful! I could not work because I lived in the bathroom. I would be sick on the way to work, at work, and on the way home. Over the following two months, I lost a lot of weight because I couldn't keep anything down. By the time I was three months pregnant, I started to feel a lot better and was able to eat again. Thank God! I was not showing at all, but my breasts were huge.

* * *

I found out about Aya's diagnosis after I had an amniocentesis around week fifteen or sixteen, which was done to determine if there were any chromosomal abnormalities or fetal infections. My doctor told me my baby had sickle cell anemia SS disease. I couldn't believe it! I wanted to scream, "OMG! Why me?"

I researched the disease, trying desperately to find out more about it. All I knew was that my brother and I had the trait. We had known since we were children. Sickle cell anemia is an inherited red blood cell disorder in which there aren't enough healthy red blood cells to carry oxygen throughout your body. Normally, red blood cells are flexible, round, and can move easily through blood vessels. In sickle cell anemia, the red blood cells are shaped like sickles or crescent moons and because they are rigid, the cells can get stuck in small blood vessels, which can slow or block blood flow and oxygen to parts of the body. Very soon after learning this heartbreaking news, I began meeting doctors at St. Luke's Hospital, Montefiore Hospital, and Hackensack Medical Center. The pediatric center at St. Luke's Hospital provided in-depth information on prevention, diagnosis, treatment, and care of conditions that affect newborns, children, and adolescents.

The center also helped me prepare for the steps to take to keep my child healthy, and I was educated about the options I would have when my child needed medical services. I met with three pediatricians and decided on Dr. Terrin. I really liked that he was affiliated with Hackensack Tomorrows Children's Institute.

When I met Dr. Terrin, I also met Judy Solomon, a social worker that introduced me to everyone at the clinic. Judy provided me with literature and information and Dr. Terrin discussed Aya's treatment and things to be mindful of and consider. Because of the disease, Aya would need ongoing treatment and care, even when she was not having a pain crisis. She had to take folic acid, essential for producing red blood cells, every day for the first two years of her life because red blood cells are turned over so quickly and the folic acid would manage and control symptoms and limit the frequency of crises.

When Aya had a pain crisis, she was treated

with pain medicines and by giving her lots of fluids every day. It was important to treat her pain right away and while non-narcotic medications were generally effective, sometimes she needed large doses of narcotics.

* * *

When Aya was born, she didn't have any complications. Her pediatrician gave her antibiotics and vaccines for the first two years of her life to help prevent any kind of infection or pain crisis. It wasn't until she was three years old that she experienced her first pain crisis. It was in her belly, and she kept saying, "It hurts, Mommy. It hurts!" It was late at night and I had to take her to the ER at Hackensack Medical Center in Hackensack, New Jersey. After she was taken into an examination room, a doctor came in and asked a lot of questions. Then, he examined her and said they would have to give her morphine for the pain along with other fluids.

"What? That medicine is too strong for her. She's only three," I said.

The doctor sat me down and explained, "She's in a lot of pain. and this medicine is protocol for children with sickle cell disease."

At the mention of those words, my heart stopped. I became emotional. I felt helpless. I wanted to carry the weight and burden of my child's pain. It was hard to witness. As a parent, not being in control is frustrating, especially when you have to sit and watch your child suffer for hours and there's nothing you can do about it but pray that the pain stops. It's the worst feeling of powerlessness.

My heart would become so heavy at times, that I wanted to break down, but I knew I couldn't because my little girl was watching me, and I had to be strong for her. I wanted to scream, cry, and go crazy, but I knew it

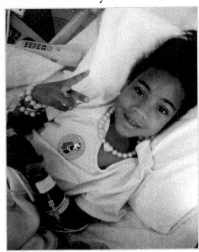

would not have changed our reality.

Often, the nurses and doctors would say or do something to upset me such as moving too slowly when Aya was clearly in pain. I wished I could jump in their shoes and take over, but my daughter might have really thought I was crazy. Sickle cell disease is so unpredictable.

CHAPTER 3

A Crisis of Pain

On a beautifully hot, sunny day, Aya and I attended her friend Danielle's birthday in New Rochelle, New York. Danielle's backyard had the greenest grass and was decorated with lots of balloons for the party. Aya was so excited about celebrating her friend's special day. Upon seeing all the decorations, she said, "I'm going to have so much fun."

During the party, Aya had a hot dog which she described as yummy. After finishing her food, she started dancing and enjoying herself in the warm sun. One minute she was playing and without warning, her eyes rolled back in her head and I saw that she was about to pass out. I caught her right before she hit the ground. She had blacked out. We took her to the car and turned on the air conditioning. I phoned her doctor and then yelled her name repeatedly. "Aya! Aya! Wake up! Wake up!"

We were on our way to the ER at Hackensack Medical Center when Aya began to regain consciousness. Hakim tried to hydrate her by giving her water. Once at the hospital, the ER doctor said Aya became overheated and was dehydrated, and that's why she'd collapsed. We waited as they gave her IV fluids.

* * *

Because Aya was so young when she had her first pain crisis, she didn't understand what was happening to her body. She didn't even know she had a disease, and as her parent, it made it even harder because I could not explain it to a toddler. I only shared with a few family members and friends that Aya had sickle cell disease because I didn't want anyone to treat her any differently than any other child or to feel sorry for her.

Aya has always been a "normal child," and I've

found people can be very ignorant about various conditions and diseases like sickle cell anemia. No one really talks about it. At least, not like they talk about leukemia and cancer. Sickle cell anemia has been swept under the rug and treated like it doesn't exist. If you ask people about it, most will just comment on the level of pain but that's it. The lack of awareness is frustrating.

When is the right time to tell family and friends? That was the hardest thing for me. Most people will never really understand how it feels to have a child with a complex blood disorder disease. Going through it is the only way most can relate. Friends and family often do not understand what a parent-caregiver goes through emotionally and physically when their child is sick. I have often said to myself, *Why me?*

Because of this disease, Aya had multiple hospital visits. Almost like clockwork, she would have a crisis once or twice a year, and the crisis was typically extremely severe. The cause for us going to the hospital was normally because of pain in her belly, legs, or arms. After checking her vitals and getting her situated, she was typically treated for her pain.

While being in the hospital for pain, she often wasn't breathing deeply and would end up developing an acute chest syndrome. Often, there were times I became really frustrated with the nurses, doctors, and respiratory therapist because the acute chest syndrome developed quickly, and when this happened, Aya developed pneumonia, which could have potentially caused lung damage over time.

It was important to stay on top of the nurses and doctors and to always be there to watch and advocate, to ensure the medicines that were given to my child were the correct medicines for her. Every child with sickle cell has a different experience. The disease affects everyone differently. Therefore, every patient is not the same and every crisis is not the same. Nurses and doctors need to be reminded from time to time that they should be more sensitive to the patient's needs, and

I would often remind them of this.

I know my child well and I have had the experience of seeing her go through many crises and have seen her body change quickly, over a matter of hours. And when I say quickly, I mean quickly! Mothers normally know their children's bodies pretty well.

We came in for pain. Then, she developed an acute chest pain. Then, she couldn't breathe. Then, her blood levels dropped and a blood transfusion was needed.

Being in the ER for hours always caused me to lose track of time because just sitting and waiting is tiring. Emotionally, it all started to get to me. I would often feel delusional and cranky after so many hours because everything took so long. I often got really annoyed and just wanted to leave, but I knew I couldn't, so I prayed instead.

My body got tired, it was usually cold, and the chairs were hard. Sometimes, I would get in the bed with Aya because I was tired of sitting in a chair, and it was comforting to be right next to her.

When I saw Aya lying in bed—fighting for her life—I would break down and cry and really understand what life is all about and appreciate this wonderful gift that was given to me. When she slept, I tried to sleep. But it was hard.

Have you ever seen your child in so much pain that it seems as if they are not there? Aya looked at me, but there was another person inside of her. She looked like her head was going to spin around. When she looked back at me because of the pain, she lunged up, screaming, "Nothing is working! I'm in so much pain! My leg! My leg!"

I sat there in the chair, staring back at her, saying to myself, *Please! Please relieve her of this pain! I can't take it!*

CHAPTER 4

Making Wishes

On September 20, 2011, we received a letter from the Make-A-Wish Foundation, which read, "We are excited to welcome you to Make-A-Wish and advise that Aya has been determined to be eligible for a wish. The Make-A-Wish foundation grants wishes for children with life-threatening medical conditions to enrich the human experience with hope, strength, and joy. A wish is powerful medicine for children who are living with the day-to-day realities of a life-threatening medical condition. A wish can rejuvenate a child and offer a new sense of inspiration, hope, and encouragement."

How exciting! There were so many possibilities! Aya had to fill out her "wish book" ahead of a volunteer meeting. The wish book was a fun way for Make-A-Wish children to give some insight into their wish requests. After the wish book was completed, the volunteers visited our home and collected the book. Aya's wish was to swim with the dolphins in the Bahamas.

A short time later, when Aya's wish list was granted, we received a message stating: "Two volunteers will be visiting your home to hear your wish." During the visit, the volunteers sat with us and completed the Make-A-Wish packet and tried to really get to know Aya better. The Wish packet was specific paperwork that allowed the volunteers to gain clarity and work with us in planning the wish. After spending several hours discussing Aya's wish, the volunteers left, optimistic about their ability to help my daughter's dream come true.

On February 13, 2012, we received a letter from Heather Kooy, senior Wish Manager for the Make-A-Wish Foundation. It read:

Dear Ms. Gibson, It was a pleasure speaking with you regarding Aya's trip to Atlantis in the Bahamas. As per our conversation, please be advised that airline reservations have been made for your family (Aya, Tyrene, Frankie (Aya's grandmother)) to travel to the Bahamas for Aya's wish. Your family is scheduled to travel Sunday, March 4th through March 8th. I have enclosed a copy of the flight itinerary for your records. I have made reservations for one room in the Beach Towers at Atlantis. We also arranged for ground transportation to and from Nassau Airport and to Atlantis. For your stay at Atlantis, we have also requested the casual dining meal plan, which includes breakfast and dinner at selected restaurants. In addition, the Make-A-Wish foundation will provide you with a chauffeur from D&G Limo to and from LaGuardia Airport and spending money to cover the cost of lunches, souvenirs, and miscellaneous expenses.

A packet containing airline tickets, spending money, transportation, etc. will be mailed to Meri and Louise, the volunteers who you met last year, approximately a week to ten days prior to the date of travel. The volunteers will contact you to make arrangements to come back to your home and to deliver the documents and go over any questions that you may *have. I will also check in with you again a few days before you leave. If you have any questions or concerns, or if there is anything I can do to make your time in the Bahamas more enjoyable, please do not hesitate to contact me. We are looking forward to the opportunity to grant Aya's wish.*

Meri and Louise came back to our home with a beautiful new suitcase and other gifts for Aya to take on her trip. We were all excited about going and Aya was excited to travel to the lush tropical island with a pristine two-mile white beach that would include barefoot, carefree, nonstop fun.

* * *

"Atlantis is your portal to a truly Bahamian experience," stated the brochure.

My mother Frankie, who Aya refers to as Nami, and I were scheduled to accompany Aya on this special trip. We received our flight itinerary and hotel reservations for one room at the Atlantis. The Make-A-Wish Foundation also provided ground transportation to and from our home to the airport and to and from the Nassau Airport and the Atlantis Hotel.

On the day of our trip, when the car service picked us up from our home, Aya was so excited about the limo ride. She couldn't believe she was going to ride in a limo to the airport. Our driver was very nice and friendly and made us comfortable throughout the ride. To be honest, I was a little scared about traveling because I was fearful that Aya might have gotten sick. I tried my best not to think about that and instead, tried to stay positive.

At the airport and on the plane, we took several pictures. Aya couldn't wait to arrive. She smiled from ear to ear as we filmed her getting her new passport stamped for the first time.

After we collected our luggage in Nassau, there was a car service waiting for us. During the car ride, Aya looked out the window, trying to see all of the sites along the way to Paradise Island, which was about a fifteen-minute ride.

When we arrived at the hotel, a special care team representative named Charris Simmons was there to greet us. She answered questions and provided a list of all the activities we could participate in during the trip. Because our room was still being prepared when we arrived, we waited in the stunning top-to-bottom lobby lounge with sun and ice. Once everything was ready, Mrs. Simmons escorted us to our room located in the Coral Towers. When we opened the door, we were met with beautiful tropical flowers, balloons, and animal-shaped towels on the beds. There was a card on a table next to one of the beds. Aya opened the card and it read: **ENJOY YOUR VACATION** on the front of the card with two glass fish. On the inside it read: "Dear Aya, Welcome to Atlantis! We do hope that the remainder of your trip will be a memorable one for you and your family. Please accept this small token on behalf of the Guest Activities Team."

A $25.00 gift card was inside, along with a list of daily activities for kids and their families.

Needless to say, we were delighted by the room, which had two queen beds. Along with the beautiful flowers, balloons, and fun towels, the décor was chic. It was accented with fresh ocean hues, soft coral pastels, and sandy golds. It was elegant, contemporary, and, most importantly, comfortable.

The bathroom had a combined shower-bathtub. A full balcony, that included a bistro set, an expansive view of the grounds, the Atlantis waterscape, and the sparkling blue ocean waters.

As soon as we got settled in, Aya wanted to get undressed and go out on the balcony to watch the sharks below our room and the beach. My mother and I wanted to rest and relax a little bit before going to have some food. We all wanted to explore Marina Village and see some of the most luxurious yachts, walk around, and see the beautiful shops and restaurants.

The Beach Tower at Atlantis is all about the beach itself. The casual, relaxed, and tropical ambiance was perfect, and it was just steps away from the Atlantis beach. The resort teemed with marine life and it was on display everywhere. The aquariums were spectacular. The rapids, water slides, and lazy river were great fun. The beach was beautiful and relaxing. Marina Village was a pretty fun place, too.

Later that evening, we were able to watch the parade, which had lots of music. Everyone was dressed in bright Bahamian costumes and masks and dancing all around the Marina Village and shops. It reminded me of Carnival. There were Bahamian pastries, coffee, ice cream, and a gelato parlor. Of course, Aya wanted to stop to have ice cream. We even walked through the Atlantis casino. Needless to say, our first night was incredibly exciting.

When we got back to our room, our housekeeper, Estelle, had the sheets pulled back with chocolates and towels on each bed shaped in animal designs. There was a note on Aya's bed that read: "Aya, I hope this puts another ray of hope and a smile on your beautiful face. Love, Estelle, Housekeeping."

* * *

Day two came really fast. We awoke early because the sun was shining brightly through our windows. We went to have breakfast in the dining marketplace, which included a made-to-order buffet.

Aya loved the strawberry-banana smoothie, and she had one each morning for breakfast while we were there. Every day, there was an array of food to choose from.  Aside from the amazing food, there were a million other activities we wanted to experience.

Aya wanted to have her hair braided in cornrows, so we went and had her hair done. From there, we headed to the pool and beach. Then, we went to the lazy river. We had a hard time trying to get Aya on the float, and while we were doing this, my bathing suit kept falling down. It all was so funny, and we all were laughing. My mother tried to take pictures and video, but had a hard time trying to work it, so I had to get back out of the water to show her. Finally, we were all on floats and able to enjoy "The Current," a mile-long river journey that took us on four-foot rolling waves, river rapids, and through mysterious caves. Winding through a tropical waterscape was fun and relaxing, especially while lying on a float without a care in the world.

From there, we headed to Atlantis Pals, where huggable pals were adopted. Aya could create her very own customized stuffed animal from scratch. She would have a brand-new friend to remind her of our incredible Atlantis vacation.

Aya chose a signature bear. She was able to hand-stuff it to make sure it had the perfect "hug factor." Then, she selected an outfit from a wide assortment of stylish and imaginative clothing and accessories. After a formal adoption to make it official, she was able to take home her very own

Atlantis Pal.

Next, we headed to Earth & Fire Pottery, where we created a one-of-a-kind masterpiece in the fun and colorful pottery studio. Aya was able to design a small bowl in the shape of a turtle, with green and white colors and her name AYA in the center. She also created a dolphin.

After that long day, we headed back to our room to relax, shower, and get ready for dinner. We wanted seafood, so we headed over to Fish, where master chef, Jose Andres's menu featured the freshest Bahamian seafood with flavors skillfully transformed into memorable dishes. The Fish dining room reflected the colors, shapes, and textures of the Bahamian seascape.

After looking at the menu, I ordered the conch fritters, hush puppies (cornbread fritters with honey), grilled grouper, tuna tartar, rice and peas, sweet plantains, and ceviche clasico (avocado, pearl onion, corn, cilantro). It was so good!

The coolest place to hang out in the evening was the ultimate teen club called Club Rush (exclusively for Atlantis guests ages 13-17) and the best part was no parents. Lol! From 7PM to 10PM, that space was loaded with cutting-edge technology, driven by immersive gaming experiences, and charged with pulsating dance floor energy. It had a live DJ and dancing, Nintendo Wii, Xbox 360 and Kinect PS3, dance competitions, game tournaments, karaoke, raffles, and prizes. It even had an exclusive teen bar that prepared specialty non-alcoholic drinks to delight the palate and keep the energy going. You could also order snacks and drinks from touchscreen menus. Crush was the ultimate teen escape at Atlantis. It was like no club anywhere else. It was modern, sleek, and sophisticated.

Aya wanted to be dropped off to go hangout and meet new friends. While she enjoyed her time with other teens, my mother and I walked around, occasionally going into shops. Eventually, we found our way into the casino and played the slots and roulette. We had a nice time. At 10PM, we headed back to Club Rush to pick up Aya. When we got there, she wasn't out yet, so we waited. When she finally came out, she looked incredibly tired, so we all walked back to the room, got undressed, and took a shower.

Before going to bed, I checked the temperature. I was a little nervous about the weather because we were going to swim with the dolphins the next day. I really was concerned with the water temperature, so before I went to bed, I prayed.

* * *

Day three was the day! We woke up early and took a relaxing twenty-minute ferry ride from Harbor Island, which took us past historic landmarks and the luxury  homes on Paradise Island, over to the dolphin encounters on Blue Lagoon Island.

Dolphin Encounters Limited on Blue Lagoon is a marine mammal facility that allows direct interaction between human participants and bottlenose dolphins. The purpose of the program is twofold—to create better appreciation of marine mammals and their environment among the general population, and to make people's lifelong dreams of swimming with dolphins come true.

Dolphin Encounters Limited strives to provide visitors with a once-in-a-lifetime experience that promotes respect, caring for dolphins and their environment, to learn more about marine mammals, and to protect these amazing animals in the wild.

When we arrived, we immediately went up a ramp and were fitted for wetsuits and water shoes. The air was cool and the water was cold. Yet, the temperature didn't concern Aya, who was so excited because she was about to swim with dolphins.

The intimate one-hour program began with a brief orientation. Then, we entered the lagoon to learn about dolphins' behavior. We were able to meet, kiss, hug, pet, and feed the dolphins in deeper water for the first half-hour of the session. The dolphins kissed Aya right on her cheek, and one of them shot water in my face. My mother enjoyed watching and recording the entire experience. We relished meeting and interacting with two of the dolphins in the most intimate and natural setting. Shallow water activities with the dolphins included an amazing dorsal tow, star turns, cradling and kissing the dolphin, as well as an exciting foot-push with a boogie board. Aya went flying up when the dolphin pushed her up on the boogie board. Then, she had to swim back to the deck. The memorable dolphin interactive programs allowed us to play with these intelligent mammals in the ultimate experience.

After the dolphin swim, we relaxed in a hammock under swaying palm trees, and went swimming in the clear turquoise lagoon. Disaster struck when, while Nami was lying in a hammock, she was bitten by a non-poisonous insect. After that ordeal, we were ready to go back to the boat to head to the hotel. By the time we reached the Atlantis, the area where Nami  had been bitten had turned red and started to swell.

Without a doubt, we'd had a really eventful and memorable day. Once we arrived back at the hotel, we wanted to relax a bit and shower before heading back out. We went out to dinner at Mesa Grill (Bobby Flay's restaurant that features southwest cuisine with a Bohemian twist). The food was delicious.

* * *

On day four, we had more adventures to look forward to. Aya had signed up for the climbers' rush. From a one-time climb to a full hour of instruction, she'd be able to climb to her heart's content across several surfaces and challenges. Aya received an award for reaching a peak and conquering the wall.

After that, she wanted to head to the tattoo artist to get an airbrush tattoo of her name written in Chinese characters. From there, we headed to the culinary adventure center, and Aya joined other budding chefs in a state-of-the-art kitchen created just for kids. The incredible 800-square-foot kitchen seated up to twenty-one kids, each with their own set of colorful tools. The surroundings and tools made each participant feel like a real chef. Aya was provided with her own tie-on apron and chef's hat. She learned how to make a key lime pie.

When her class was over, she provided me with a small key lime pie that was so delicious, my mother and I ate the whole pie! Aya didn't get any but told us she had so much fun taking her culinary class.

We headed over to the Mayan Temple because Aya wanted to plummet down the five daring slides of the iconic temple. This leap of faith took Aya on a near-vertical plunge into shark-infested waters. She slid and floated through the tunnels and the caves of the Jungle Slide. I was scared to get on the slide. However, I had to go with Aya. I screamed all the way down while Aya was cracking up, laughing at me. We hung out at the beach and pool for the rest of the afternoon recognizing that we were leaving the next day.

That night, Charris Simmons left a letter in our room that read, in part:

I am sad to see you leave, but as you prepare this wonderful evening to leave paradise, keep in mind that checkout time in the morning is at 11AM. If you require a late check out, please make us aware.

Of course, we wanted a late check out and made them aware that we did.

We sincerely hope that you have enjoyed your trip to the fullest and made memories that can change your life for the better. Why Me? What a wonderful name for your book. I hope, one day, that I can read that book and smile because I had the opportunity to know you when you were just writing it. You have made a life-changing impact on my life, and I hope that we have done the same for you, so please keep in contact with us, and we will do the same with you.

From my heart to yours,
Your Special Care Concierge,
—Charris Simmons

CHAPTER 5

Going to Camp

Hole in the Wall Gang Camp was not like any other camp. It is named after the gang in Newman's film *Butch Cassidy and the Sundance Kid*. The nonprofit residential summer camp and year-round service center is dedicated to providing "a different kind of healing" to seriously ill children and their families throughout the northeast, free of charge. It's a community that celebrates the fun, friendship, and spirit of childhood, where every child can "raise a little hell," and it ensures that children with serious medical conditions have a chance to experience the world of possibilities that camp has to offer.

When Aya and I first drove up to the entrance of the camp, we both said, "Wow!"

The camp is nestled within 300 acres of land, including forty-four acres of a lake. There were fifteen perfect little cabins in five color-coded units: blue, yellow, red, white, and green. They offered horseback riding, an Olympic-sized heated pool, lounge, infirmary, arts and crafts, woodshop, sports and recreation, dining hall, theater, archery, a tree house, a boat house, and a lake. There was an expro or exploration program which is where the older campers can go to relax. It houses the outdoor pizza oven, hammocks, and Frisbee golf.

I was ecstatic that Aya could finally go swimming in a pool that was heated to 90 degrees and warm enough for her to enjoy. While fishing, Aya caught a snapping turtle that kept crawling up her fishing line. She learned how to feed and care for a horse as well as ride one, including a loop around the ring and walking along wooded trails. She even attended a horse wedding! Aya is very competitive and won medals in fishing, archery, and horseback riding while she was there.

Aya's letter from camp:

Dear Mom,

I miss you. I've been a little homesick. I tried to call you, but they wouldn't let me call you. Sometimes, I cry because I am so sad because I can only write letters to you and can never call you. I hope you got my first sent-away letter. Hope you like it. I miss you. Send me a letter back.

Of course, I called the camp and left a message, and Aya's camp counselor called me back with Aya on the phone. We were both missing each other and were glad we could talk, even though she wasn't able to talk long.

CHAPTER 6

A Cure for Aya

When Aya and I were in the clinic one day, I overheard Dr. Gilio talking to a patient about receiving a bone marrow transplant. Aya heard this, too, and said, "Mommy, I want to be cured."

I looked at her and said, "Let's see if you would be a candidate to receive one."

We asked Dr. Gilio and he indicated that we would need to set up an appointment with his office, so we did. During the subsequent meeting, we were told that Aya was not a candidate because she was not sick enough given she was only having a pain crisis about once or twice a year.

I said to myself, *Damn! How sick do you need to be?* I didn't want to hear anything short of a resounding "yes." This was unacceptable to me and made us feel frustrated with the doctor and the whole healthcare system, but we continued pursuing and pushing Dr. Gilio and his team every time we had a chance.

I did not want Aya to be placed on maintenance medication because it was a temporary solution for her permanent problem and I wanted her to be cured. Aya's pain crises would cause her to be admitted to the hospital for extended periods of time. These extended stays often resulted in her developing pneumonia from being in a hospital bed for a long time.

Dr. Jennifer Krajewski, a pediatric stem cell transplantation specialist at Hackensack Meridian Joseph M. Sanzari Children's Hospital, indicated that these episodes were frequent and served as an indicator that a transplant was a good option. Dr. Krajewski worked under Dr. Gilio and was brought in due to expansions within the stem cell transplant team.

By the time Aya was eleven, Dr. Krajewski recommended her for a bone marrow transplant.

Because she did not have a family member that matched her, the donor would have to come from the National Marrow Donor Program or NMDP, which included the Be The Match Registry.

"Unrelated donor transplants are trickier, and there is a higher frequency of complications. This is why we currently only offer this procedure to patients with severe symptoms," Dr. Krajewski explained, saying that donors are rated on an eight-to-ten scale.

A meeting was set for July 17, 2011. This would include the whole team and staff, which consisted of doctors, residents, APNs, RNs, nutritionists, social workers, child life, psychology and education related to the study. However, other medical specialties that might be consulted or involved with Aya's care included: infectious disease, surgical team, gastroenterology, pediatric intensivists, and neurology, among others. Every member of this team was essential to the success of Aya's transplant and post-care needs. Therefore, they needed to be included in her treatment. Their goal, as a team, was to cure Aya while providing adequate support to the parents and those caretakers that would support her during this time.

We also discussed a low microbial diet and nutrition guidelines post-transplant for Aya because a decrease in immune function due to chemotherapy could lead to the risk of developing a food-related infection. Given this, a list of "eat and do not eat" foods was provided along with home sanitation and food storage guidelines. We were also given a daily list of medications that Aya was required to take, which included shots in her leg before the transplant. Aya, Hakim, and I received a ten-page consent form which detailed vital information about what was ahead so we could make plans and decisions. We went, step by step, over every page.

I asked Dr. Krajewski several questions. I even asked how many casualties there had been. Aya asked a lot of questions as well including if she could pick where her port would go. She was concerned about having a scar on her chest, so she asked if it could be put on her side, right below her breast. Aya also asked if she would have her own room to which Dr. Krajewski replied, "Yes, Aya, you will have a suite with your own bathroom because you will need to stay in that room for a month or possibly, longer."

Dr. Krajewski wanted us to take the paperwork home and discuss it before deciding to commit. Also included in the agreement was an effort to coordinate appropriate services for my child during the process of Bone Marrow Transplant (BMT). It is imperative to have your full cooperation as a parent because a BMT is a rigorous procedure that requires significant parental involvement, particularly during the weeks following transplant.

Post-transplant, Aya would be closely monitored inpatient and would require numerous interventions that may be deemed necessary. It was hard even imagining my child receiving a transplant. Aya, Hakim, and I had to be prepared to allow for these supportive interventions. We all had to sign the consent form indicating that we understood and were on board with moving forward.

In October of 2011, we started to prepare for testing for the transplant. Aya was also struggling and had a very difficult time at the start of the process. There was a lot of typing that needed to be done, and she was scared of needles. Typing human leukocyte antigen (HLA) is used to match patients with donors for a bone marrow transplant. There were fifteen vials of blood that had to be collected from Aya and entered into the data bank. HLAs are proteins or markers found on most cells. Doctors look for a donor who matches their patient's tissue type.

It was difficult, but we got through it. Aya was fortunate to have three matches on the registry, but the journey to transplant was not easy. Unfortunately, Aya's first donor did not show up when it was time to be tested again. Because the first donor backed out, we decided to wait and work with Aya to help with her fear of needles. Counselors and nurses worked with her for several months to help her overcome this fear.

In February 2012, before our trip to The Bahamas, Aya had one of her worst pain crises ever. I wasn't sure she was going to make it. The pain was so severe that nothing worked to alleviate it. She developed an infection and had a severe fever and pneumonia. The pain meds were not taking the pain away, and her oxygen levels were low. I wished it was me. All I wanted as her mother was to take all of the pain away. Being by her side, unable to fix things caused me to feel helpless and broken. The situation was dark and too hard to deal with alone, but I did. Being in the hospital room, day after day, night after night, a week went by, and that made me want to write down my feelings. I found it therapeutic and comforting to vent my frustrations.

Being a caregiver changed some areas of my life. I had a different way of thinking. Financially, it was a burden because I could not really work when Aya was sick. I often wished I had someone to talk to because most people didn't seem to understand or want to understand what Aya and I were going through. My mother was a blessing. She came to stay with us for a year, which allowed me to work and leave to go home, just to take a shower and have some time to myself and unwind. Family and friends that I thought would have been there, weren't. Unfortunately, back then, there were not many support groups for caretakers and the dynamics were draining, overwhelming, and lonely.

Around that time, about six months after her first donor backed out along with a second donor that never responded, we decided to try a donor search for a third time. In May 2012, we received a letter from Dr. Jennifer Krajewski stating: "Your doctor is considering a marrow or cord blood stem cell transplant from an unrelated donor as a treatment option for your child's disease." It went on to say: "We want to help you understand the next steps and process and to get answers for any questions you may have."

When a doctor is considering a transplant using

an unrelated donor for a child's disease, now or in the future, he or she consults the NMDP which operates the Be The Match Registry and provides volunteer donors and cord blood units for people who need a transplant but do not have a related donor. NMDP has a team that provides support for families of a child who may need a transplant or who have already received a transplant. They are available for patients, caregivers, family members and friends, at any time.

Before a bone marrow transplant, certain tests are required which meant Aya had to go through a series of procedures. These include, a chest X-ray, blood tests, PET scan, heart tests, and a bone marrow biopsy. Donors are also expected to complete certain tests. Aya had to provide fifteen valves of blood that were needed before transplant.

There really would not be any negotiations in terms of Aya's needs which may include but not be limited to a list of twelve items that were provided. Changes may occur at any point during a child's medical care, therefore, medical decisions and treatments will have to be adjusted to accommodate or reflect the changes.

We prepared Aya's suite. We brought her favorite pillow cover and blanket and all of her yarn to make friendship bracelets. Her room was decorated with a pink art piece that said "Good Luck, Aya" in large bold writing, which was decorated with colored feathers and beautiful turtles, dolphins, crabs, and

sea horses with all kinds of well wishes from family, friends, and hospital staff. There was also a yoga mat, a chart to count down the amount of days left to stay in hospital, and a big teddy bear that was almost as big as Aya. My daughter's suite was very bright, had a great view, and included a nice TV, so she would be able to watch a variety of shows and movies.

A blood or marrow transplant is the only known cure for SCD. It is not surgery, rather a treatment that takes a donor's healthy blood-forming cells and puts them into the patient's bloodstream, where they begin to grow and make healthy red blood cells, white blood cells, and platelets. To help with the administration of medicines, blood transfusions and obtaining blood for lab tests, a central venous catheter (also known as a Hickman or Broviac catheter) would be placed before the transplant, which Aya wanted placed in a specific location so as to avoid having a scar on her chest. This was a hollow tube that was inserted by a surgeon or radiologist, usually in an operating room.

On June 28, 2012, at 8:15 AM, Aya was taken to have the Broviac catheter line placement. I asked to speak to the anesthesiologist before she took Aya in and asked if she'd had a good night's sleep and if I could go into the procedure room to watch them put Aya to sleep. The doctor allowed me to go in but once the anesthesia was administered, I had to leave. I prayed so much while I was waiting. I was a nervous wreck!

Aya received two rounds of high doses of chemotherapy to prepare her body for the transplant to prevent her immune system from rejecting the donor cells. I would try to keep Aya's mind off treatment by keeping her laughing. One day, I slid into a split, and both of us laughed so hard. Aya told me not to do that again because it was hurting her side.

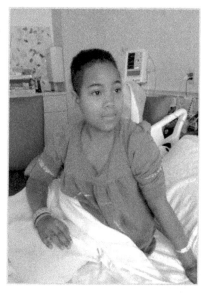

During the process, Aya had an allergic reaction to Cefepime, one of the medications. Thank God I was there because she flipped out. Her face was red, itchy, and hives were all over her body. All she could do was scream.

I immediately got help from the nurse who had to give her a shot to stop the negative reaction. Aya also had an adverse reaction to Tylenol® with Codeine, which caused nausea and 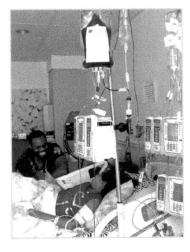 vomiting. Next, her hair began to fall out and become frizzy and brittle. Aya said it was itchy, so I suggested we cut it into a cute, short style. She agreed even though we both knew she would lose most of her hair.

* * *

The big transplant day was August 1, 2012, a day I will never forget. We had the priest come and we (Hakim, Nami, and I) prayed over Aya before the transplant started. The large bag of bone marrow from her donor had to be flown from Cologne,

Germany, within forty-eight hours of when it was collected from the donor. (There are owners of private planes that donate this service for free.) Aya's doctor commented that Aya's donor must have been a large German man because the bag was full of bone marrow. It took eight hours for the bone marrow to be intravenously placed into Aya's arm.

We were all so tired that day especially Aya who took several naps. Any time someone entered her room, they had to put on a gown and a mask, and wash their hands, so germs would not enter the room.

Aya asked her doctors, if it went well, if she could go home on August 16, 2012, before her birthday, which was six days later. Her doctors said they would see how her body reacted to the bone marrow transplant.

Well, the transplant was a success. Fifteen days after the transplant, and before her birthday, Aya was allowed to go home with a list of discharge instructions, even though we still had to go back to the hospital every week. We had to be back at the doctor's office on August 16, 2012.

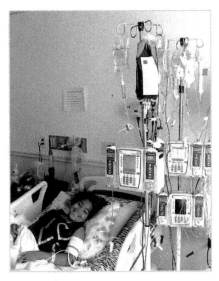

A nurse came to our home three times the first week and twice a week for the following three weeks to flush Aya's central line and provide care that included changing her catheter dressing and making sure she was doing okay. There was also a list of several medications for Aya to take daily, which would help stop her body from rejecting the transplant. During this time, Aya had to follow the nutrition guidelines for people with decreased immune function due to chemotherapy and who were at risk of developing a food-related infection so we had a list of foods she could eat and foods she could not eat. She could only drink bottled water, and personal hygiene and oral care were very important. Aya had to be homeschooled from September 2012 to January 2013.

In September, while Aya was being homeschooled, I arranged for Sarah Donnangelo, the educational coordinator at the hospital, to meet with the principal, guidance counselor, and me to discuss Aya's tutoring plan and schedule. I also advocated for the Fort Lee schools to provide Skype so Aya could stay connected with teachers, lessons, etc. The school district had never had such a request and denied it because they thought it would cause a security issue for other students in Aya's class. So I countered by given them a clear plan of what needed to be done. Essentially, the camera could be placed on the teacher, not the students, and parents should receive a note informing them that it was only being done in the class Aya attended. My request was denied twice before finally being approved by Fort Lee school's interim superintendent, Dr. Sharon Amato.

Aya continued home schooling, and after a

couple of months of advocating, she was doing very well after transplant until October 15, 2012. She had a fever and became very sick quickly and was admitted to the hospital. She had an episode of septicemia. All three lumens of her central line grew Klebsiella, Acinetobacter, and Pantea (which was negative bacteria in her blood that caused her to be sick). The line was removed, and she recovered after a few days, following a course of antibiotics. Aya also had to be put on high doses of hydrocortisone because she suffered from adrenal insufficiency. Then, she was transitioned back to prednisone. She had repeated tests done in January 2013 and was able to be weaned off the steroids.

Aya continued to have very red lips that were discolored. Sometimes, they would swell and become dry. This was a result of graft versus host disease (GVHD), an attack by the donor cells against the recipient's body. We also had to start re-immunization of vaccines because all of the previous vaccines were wiped out from the chemotherapy.

CHAPTER 7

Slowly Making Progress

In January 2013, Aya was able to return to school in person. She was excited to be social with other students again, even though she knew people might look at her differently because her hair was short and the prednisone had made her look bloated in the face, especially in her cheeks, and stomach. Her skin color was also a little pinkish. Aya was fearful about not being able to enjoy certain recreational activities at school.

We tried to wean her off the prednisone. However, her body kept reacting negatively when the dose was too low. Then, we would have to up the dose again before trying to lower it for a few months. We worked with a pediatric endocrinology doctor named Dr. Granny at Hackensack University Medical Center.

It was hard for Aya to keep up with school but she continued to work with the tutors so she would not fall behind in her studies. During her winter/Easter break, we decided to visit my cousins, Ernest and Annamarie, in Orlando, Florida, and go to Disney Universal.

While we were having so much fun, we received a call from Dr. Krajewski, who informed us that a test that had been taken before we left showed that Aya had an infection. We had to provide the name of a pharmacy that was near where we were staying, so she could send the prescription there because Aya needed to start taking the medication right away. This made me nervous because I thought to myself, *We are away from her doctors. Please don't let Aya get sick now.*

Aya started taking the medication, and we enjoyed the rest of our time in Orlando. After seven days, her infection went away. She continued taking prednisone for one year after the transplant. After her transplant, Aya continued having tearing in her right eye and had to have the tear duct opened to help stop the tearing.

CHAPTER 8

Full Circle Moments

We were interested in finding out more about Aya's donor but a requirement of Be the Match® was having to wait for two years before we were allowed to sign a post-transplant consent form to release personal information. Both parties had to sign the form before either party could contact the other. Melanie Nycz, Aya's APN, provided us with the form we signed and emailed it to Barbara Adler-Brecher, who worked for the office of patient advocacy, patient services for Be The Match.

On October 10, 2014, we received an email from Aya's donor Marc Schemmann. It read:

Dear Aya,
We hope you feel well nowadays. This is Marc from

Germany. You might already recognize the name by an information letter from the bone marrow agency. I was the guy who was so glad to be able to help you by giving you some stem cells.

At that time in August 2012, when the bone marrow donation center in Cologne, Germany, asked for my help, I did not hesitate to go into their hospital.

To see that I am able to help someone by a "small" gift to get better in health was a great honor.

Now, in September 2014, I was extremely happy to hear from the bone marrow agency that you are still feeling fine and that you have asked for a contact address. :)

So let me introduce myself and my family. I am Marc, thirty-three years old, from a town called Unna in West Germany.

Maybe you have heard something about the city of Cologne or perhaps Amsterdam? Both are not far away, although Amsterdam is already in the Netherlands. I am working in retail in a big office near my hometown.

I am living here with my wife Sabrina. She is a German and English teacher at a comprehensive school. And for a short time with my newborn daughter Nele.

Nele is eleven weeks old, and our biggest pride and joy. Also, Nele is the reason why I haven't been able to mail earlier as she had some problems with her belly and her growth. It keeps our complete concentration and efforts in the last weeks. Now she is feeling a bit better. Additionally, we have two cats which are called Tigger and Sushi. Together we are living in a rented flat.

Our hobbies, besides our baby and our cats, are movies of nearly every genre and watching or playing soccer or playing party games of any kind with our friends.

Soccer is my most favourite sport in Germany, and we support a team which is called Borussia Dortmund.

Nowadays, we are often on a walk with Nele in her baby carriage/kinderwagen, as these are the last days we are able to do such walks. From October onwards, we have to expect more cold and wet temperatures in Germany till February/ March next year. Ok. This was our first small introduction, who we are, where we live and so on.

We are excited to hear from you. Attached you can find a picture of us three to have a first view and impression.

Have a nice day. Hope to hear from you.

Best regards,

Marc

Aya responded with an email:

Hi, Marc,

This is Aya. Thank you so much for getting in touch with me and my mom. We are both very grateful. First, I would like to say, just by even considering to donate, makes you an amazing man, and by you helping me, you're an outstanding man that had such an impact on my life. You don't understand how amazing it is to be sickle-cell free, healthy, and happy. I feel like my life just turned around, and I started all over again, but I would love to talk more to you and your wife and your cute little baby. She's adorable, but anyway, do you have FaceTime or Skype? I would love to have a one-on-one talk if that's ok with you. Thank you so much. Just reading what you wrote just brought me to tears. I hope that, one day, maybe, I could be as brave as you were to help a little kid out like you did for me. This was the picture when I was receiving the bone marrow transplant and after chemo.

I hope you have a very good day. I hope to talk soon!

Xoxo, Aya and Mom (Tyrene)

Marc responded with an email back to us:

Hey, Aya,

Good evening from Germany :)

It is nearly 9 PM, and we have been successful lulling our daughter to sleep. She is so sweet but bringing her to bed…it's, sometimes, like a fight :-)

You cannot imagine how glad I am to hear that you are feeling better. Btw thx for your picture. Your words and first view developing goose bumps on my skin. I have always mentioned to donate agency that, if they need any further cells, I come back to hospital at once. Since I have a little daughter, my responsibility for life and care grow from day to day.

Thx for your offer to chat via Skype or FaceTime. Yes, we would love to talk to you one-on-one via Skype. My wife as English teacher is very excited to chat with you as native English speaker, too. Hope my English is comprehensible. I am working in retail office and often have to chat and mail with Far East in English.

Let's see what's best time to chat due to time difference of six hours. I am working till 5-6 PM CET. After my return each evening starts in same sequence...

Eating, playing with Nele, bringing/ singing sweetie to sleep together with my wife. From approximately 8 PM CET till 10 PM onwards, we have free time to chill & chat if you like. Are you able to catch a chat such early in the afternoon? Or do you wish to chat any later? In case we could settle our first chat on next weekend. We definitely will find our time. Pls keep us updated about your possible chat time options, too. I would appreciate if we could start to try our first chat from Tuesday onwards at any day.

Recently, I am trying to cure a flu, and my voice is little bit weak. But till Monday, I should have renewed my strength. OK, I wish you and your mom a nice Saturday and look forward to hearing from you soon.

Best wishes from us,
Marc & Sabrina (and Nele)

* * *

We sent emails back and forth until we were able

to speak via video. We spoke several times with Marc and his wife Sabrina. They even had a picture of Aya in their home.

Aya was invited by her Spanish teacher, Ms. Acosta, to attend a Germany-in-Depth trip by Educational Tours. From July 2 - 10, 2016, they would visit Berlin, Dresden, Munich, Rothenberg, Heidelberg, and Lucerne.

I emailed Marc in advance to inform him that Aya would be going to Germany on a school trip and would love to meet and thank him in person for saving and changing her life. In the email, I attached her touring schedule and informed him that Aya's teacher was aware that Aya would love to meet him and would make arrangements for this to happen. I asked him to let me know if it was possible with his schedule.

Marc agreed to meet Aya at a restaurant in Heidelberg. Four years after transplant, and on day eight of her trip, on July 9, 2016, Aya woke up in Heidelberg, Germany and began walking to meet the stranger who changed her life. Aya said she felt anxious and excited to meet the person that meant so much to her. She walked through Heidelberg with her teacher to find the restaurant, thinking about what she would say and how to act. This was the moment she had been waiting for and dreamt about and brought a plane ticket for. It was the moment she would finally explain a pain-free life to the person who most needed to hear about it. That day marked an important day as Aya embarked on a major milestone of her journey—meeting Marc Schemmann and Sabrina.

Aya arrived looking for a complete stranger. She saw Marc and Sabrina across the street and waved. They embraced on the street and afterwards, joined Aya and her teacher inside the restaurant for what promised to be an awkward lunch conversation. The first thing Aya did was thank him for his bone marrow. Getting to know someone in an hour seems hard, but Aya said she felt like she'd known him her entire life.

Ms. Acosta captured their embrace on camera and as I watched it later, seeing that moment caused tears to flow. I cried because it was an emotional day and I could clearly see how everything had come full circle.

Eight years ago, Marc—a stranger—changed Aya's life forever through his donation. Aya was grateful she was able to thank him in person and share how he saved and ultimately, changed her life. None of it would have been possible without them, God, and Be The Match®. They gave Aya a new life and proved that with God, everything is possible!

Epilogue

<u>In Aya's Words</u>

I would like to become a pediatrician because I believe it is something I could enjoy doing for the rest of my life and I would be helping patients through their pain and suffering. I have dedicated my studies and life to becoming a doctor. I want to give back to children who are like me. My dedication is very different from

others which enables me to relate to and understand my patients more than a physician that isn't as connected through personal experience. Through my own personal experience with spending years in and out of hospitals, my own pain and suffering, and working with many doctors and nurses, I see things from a unique perspective.

I was born with sickle cell anemia, which is a blood disorder. I went through a bone marrow transplant at the age of eleven, and from that time, I've learned so much about the medical field through living it. I've been around many healthcare providers and since the age of seven, I've wanted to become a pediatrician. Although the road to becoming a pediatrician is long, they are very smart, hardworking, gentle-hearted, and amazing people.

From the Author

Mothering the Crescent Moons as a title is grounded in the reality of my journey. The act of mothering implies nurturing, protecting, and guiding. As Aya's mother, my instincts often kicked in when I didn't have expertise or even understanding to rely on after my daughter's diagnosis and throughout the process up to her receiving a life-changing transplant. In sickle cell anemia, the red blood cells are shaped like sickles or crescent moons. The title is beyond fitting.

When I consider everything that's happened, I recognize the profound impact Be the Match® has had on my life, as well as my daughter's life. Since Aya's transplant, we have continued to raise awareness for the program by volunteering at donor drives, taking part in fundraisers, speaking engagements, speaking to families that are thinking about going to transplant, and championing advocacy efforts.

Aya is currently on the Tackle Kids with

Cancer.org website. This campaign shares patients' stories that help to raise funds for patients.

Currently, Aya is a student at Loyola University in New Orleans where she is studying biology with the hopes of becoming a pediatric hematologist, like Dr. Terrin. In fact, she is so inspired by his work that she spent time during the summer shadowing him and learning first-hand. Additionally, Aya is involved with Be the Match®, the largest online registry for bone marrow and stem cell transplants. Aya speaks with families to provide guidance, shares her story with others, and organizes donor drives.

I serve as the New Jersey Ambassador Advocate for the Be The Match® National Marrow Donor program. I received a certificate of recognition for being an outstanding ambassador for our mission to save lives through cellular therapy.

Be The Match® is an exemplary program and it's important for people to support the organization's work. I would also like to bring more awareness to families that have sickle cell that they, too, can be cured. We need to have more conversations about sickle cell in general, especially within the Black community. Many couples get together and do not discuss whether they have the trait or disease, not knowing that their children may be affected. It's important for society to be educated about this disease, just like we are with cancer and leukemia.

Lastly, I would like to give advice to the parents and caregivers of children who have medical conditions that are difficult to treat. I have summarized this advice into six principles that have served me well:

1. *Never give up.*

2. *Keep your options open.*

3. *If one door closes, look for another door or even a window. (This might require finding another doctor, expert, or specialist.)*

4. *Keep learning about new technological developments.*

5. *Ask a lot of questions.*

6. *Pray.*

(Tyrene & Aya)

*For more information on sickle cell anemia, visit
TackleKidsCancer.org and BeTheMatch.org.*

You can also find Aya's story at
https://www.tacklekidscancer.org/team/meet-aya/